THE DINOSAUR'S COLD

AH-CHOO

The dinosaur woke
with a cold in his head.
He sneezed and he sneezed,
then he climbed out of bed.

2

He sniffed and he sniffed,
then he sat down to think.
"What I need most
is a hot lemon drink."

3

"I've no lemons," he said.
"I'll go to the store."
So he put on his hat
and walked out the door.

As he opened the door,
he met young Willy White,
who was holding the string
of a long yellow kite.

"Hello," Willy said.
"How do you do?"
The dinosaur sneezed
and said, "Ah — Choo!" 7

Crossing the bridge
he met old Mr. Plat,
on his way to the vet
with his big spotted cat.

8

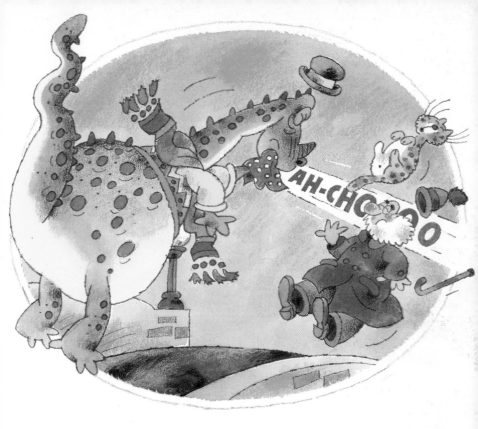

"Hello," he said.

"How do you do?"

The dinosaur sneezed

and said, "Ah — Choo!"   9

Around the first bend,
he met Roly the dog
with Jason and John,
who were out for a jog.

"Hello," they said.
"How do you do?"
The dinosaur sneezed
and said, "Ah — Choo!"

11

As he got to the store,
he met Penny and Pam,
who were doing the shopping
with their brother Sam.

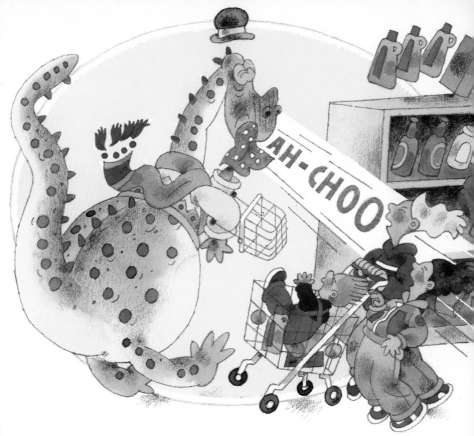

"Hello," they said.
"How do you do?"
The dinosaur sneezed
and said, "Ah — Choo!"

13

He bought a big lemon
from kind Mr. Ned.
Then he made a hot drink
and he went back to bed.

At the end of the week,
he felt much better.
He went into town
to mail a letter.

15

He said to the people,
"How do you do?"
Everyone sneezed and said,
16 "AH — CHOO!"